COMPUTERS IN THE DVLC:

a data processing case study

The material in this students' booklet was produced using funds from the government-sponsored Microelectronics Education Programme (MEP).

The written material was prepared by D. McPhee and subsequent editing was carried out by members of the ICL Computer Education in Schools Project (ICL-CES). The study was prepared with the agreement of DVLC but teachers should note that it provides only a simplified illustration of the work of the centre. The procedures described may change from time to time.

A separate booklet containing notes for teachers is also available.

ISBN 0 903885 27 1

Printed by:
ICL Printing Services, Letchworth, Hertfordshire.

Published by:
ICL Computer Education in Schools, 60 Portman Road, Reading, Berkshire.

COMPUTERS IN THE DVLC:

a data processing case study

by

D. McPHEE

Contents

Chapter 1: Origins of the DVLC

Throughout its history the motor car has been the subject of legislation designed to give the government some control over the use of road vehicles. One of the earliest laws was the controversial 'Red Flag Act' of 1865 requiring that a vehicle on the road should be preceded by a man on foot carrying a red flag. Furthermore, the speed of the vehicle was limited to 2 mph in towns and 4 mph in the country. Despite protests, the act remained in force for more than 30 years until 1896 when light cars were permitted to travel at 12 mph.

Since that time the number and complexity of motoring regulations have increased dramatically. For the purposes of this study we are interested in three particular items of legislation.

Firstly, in 1903, an act of Parliament was passed which required all motor vehicles on the road to be registered. Thus every vehicle on British roads, with very few exceptions, must have a registration mark displayed on the number plate. The mark is simply a means of identifying a vehicle and tracing the owner, or the 'registered keeper'.

Eighteen years later, in 1921, all motor vehicles on British roads had to be licenced. The licence is usually referred to as a 'tax disc' and must be displayed on the windscreen. Vehicle excise licensing is merely a way of collecting taxes on vehicles. Historically a vehicle tax was thought necessary to help pay for building and upkeep of roads. These days the taxation is paid directly into the coffers of the Exchequer.

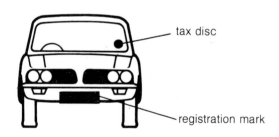

tax disc

registration mark

The third act to concern us was passed in 1930 when all drivers of vehicles in Britain were required to hold driving licences. Every vehicle driver must be licensed to ensure that vehicles are driven only by people who are medically fit and entitled to drive. Licensing also exists to prevent persons who have been disqualified by the courts, for various reasons, from driving vehicles. Driver licensing plays a major role in our road safety arrangements. The fee charged only covers administration costs.

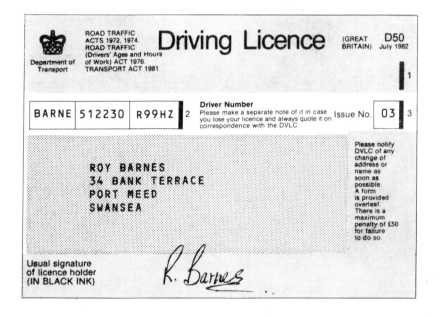

These Acts of Parliament led to the setting up of a manual clerical system to deal with all vehicle and driver records, a system which lasted until 1970.

Licensing before computerisation

The main problem with the old vehicle licensing system was that when the owner of a vehicle moved to a different area or sold his vehicle to someone living elsewhere, the records had to be transferred from one local office to another. This led to millions of folders containing individual vehicle details being circulated annually amongst the different local offices.

This clerical system had several shortcomings:

—it was wasteful of time and very expensive;

—there was difficulty in tracing vehicle records quickly if an enquiry was made;

—because the local offices were all working independently of each other, it was not difficult for a disqualified driver to apply for a new driving licence to another local office and to obtain it by making a false declaration.

Another factor which led to the setting up of a computerised system was the rapid growth in the number of road users. During the 1960s there was a 50% increase in the number of drivers, and a 60% increase in the number of vehicles. By the mid-sixties the system had reached saturation point and there was every indication that the future would see even more dramatic increases.

A government working party in 1965 recommended to the Minister of Transport that an entirely new system should be set up to replace the existing organisation. The working party advised that the new system should have a central office of considerable size, with Automatic Data Processing Facilities. As a result of these recommendations the DVLC was opened in 1970.

The DVLC is situated at Morriston, approximately five miles from the centre of Swansea. It was set up to centralise the functions of driver and vehicle licensing, formerly carried out by approximately 200 local offices, and consists of four buildings sited on a hill overlooking the M4 motorway. About 4,000 people are employed at the centre and other DVLC offices in Swansea.

The computerised system for driving licences became operational in Spring 1973. The vehicle registration system went live in Autumn 1974 with the licensing and registration of all new vehicles. The records of all other vehicles on the road before that date have been transferred to the DVLC, and on file at the centre are all the details of currently licensed vehicles.

The system has changed quite a lot since its early days; its main function now is to maintain and update the vehicle and driver records.

The DVLC computer system has the following functions:

1   To maintain an accurate register of the details of all vehicles registered in the U.K. and their current keepers.

2   To collect vehicle excise duty.

3   To maintain road safety by ensuring that a valid vehicle test certificate (M.O.T.) is in order when the vehicle is licensed.

4   To provide the Home Office (Police National Computer) with details of all vehicles registered, and any change in ownership of vehicle particulars.

5   To produce renewal reminders for vehicles whose licence is about to expire.

6   To maintain statistical records for use in forward planning.

7   To answer enquiries about vehicle registration records from keepers and other persons entitled to make such enquiries. This includes helping manufacturers trace keepers of defective vehicles — a fee is payable to the DVLC for certain enquiries.

We can see from the diagram on page 6 that the processing of both registration and driver licences are essentially the same. Therefore this study will concentrate on a description of the registration processing system only. Please note that the vehicle excise licensing system, and the driver and vehicle licence reminder systems are not described.

Exercise

During the 1960s, the manual registration and licensing system was causing problems. Imagine you were a systems analyst engaged in carrying out a feasibility study. Write your initial report indicating the benefits, and possibly the drawbacks, of computerisation.

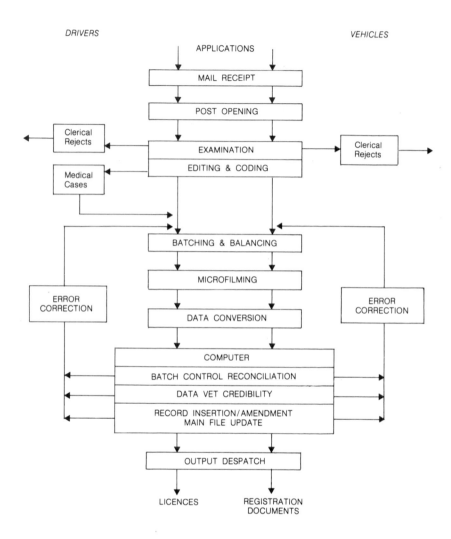

Processing of applications at DVLC

Chapter 2: The vehicle registration system

The purpose of the registration system is to maintain a central record of all registered vehicles in the UK, which includes the name and address of the keeper of each vehicle. The system is run using batch processing with files held on magnetic tape. Source data is collected daily in batches of 100 documents. Each weekday these batches are processed by the computer section, the run commencing early in the evening and continuing through the night. We will now have a look in some detail at the way in which this system operates.

Data Files

There are two files involved in the vehicle registration system. One is the main file (master file) containing details of all vehicles registered in Britain. In order to keep it up to date a transaction file is used containing details of any changes to be made to the main file. A new transaction file is created every day.

The vehicle main file

The vehicle main file consists of a very large number of records which contain relevant information about particular vehicles. Within each record are fields such as registration number, make, model, name of keeper etc. The file consists of 150 reels of magnetic tape and its function is to hold a record of every vehicle registered in Great Britain. Records are held in order of vehicle registration mark as this mark is the key by which any particular record can be located. The table on page 9 shows part of the contents of a vehicle main file record. Additional information held would include:

— wheelplan of vehicle — 4 wheels, 6 wheels etc.;

— type of fuel — petrol, diesel;

— chassis/frame number;

— engine number;

— gross weight.

Part of a vehicle main file record

Field	Length	Description	Example
1	7	registration mark	EGL144W
2	7	vehicle make	FORD
3	8	model	FIESTA
4	6	colour	BROWN
5	4	engine size	1000
6	1	taxation class	P
7	16	name of current keeper	JANE GRANT
8	30	address of current keeper	14 MEADOW WAY GRANTHAM WILTSHIRE
9	16	name of previous keeper	MARTIN WOOD
10	30	address of previous keeper	2 HILL VIEW

Main file records are stored serially on magnetic tape.

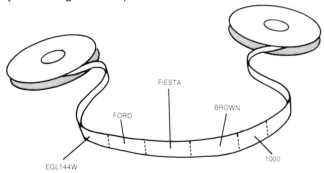

FIESTA

FORD

BROWN

1000

EGL144W

9

The vehicle transaction file

The transaction file is used to store current data for the processing of the vehicle main file. Before each update it has to be sorted into the same record key order as the main file. We have seen that all main file records are of the same type and format. This is not the case for transaction records, which are of three distinct types:

— records to be amended on the main file, for example, a change of keeper's address or a change of vehicle colour;

— records to be deleted (removed) from the main file, for example, when a vehicle is scrapped or destroyed by accident;

— records to be inserted into the main file, for example, when a new vehicle is being registered for the first time.

In order to determine the type of record a special 'type' field is included. This field contains a single character, A, D or I, referring to amendment, deletion or insertion.

Part of a transaction record might contain the information shown in the table below. However, a 'D' type record (deletion) does not require so much information and need contain only the first two fields, type and registration mark, as shown in the table at the top of page 11.

Part of a transaction file record (insertion)

Field	Length	Description	Example
1	1	type of record	I
2	7	registration mark	MGL32Y
3	7	vehicle make	AUSTIN
4	8	model	ALLEGRO

Complete transaction file record (deletion)

Field	Length	Description	Example
1	1	type of record	D
2	7	registration mark	HAE379F

Questions

1   With reference to the example main file record on page 9:

   (a)   Which item of data distinguishes this record from all others on the file?

   (b)   What information is contained in field 5?

   (c)   Mr. Perrin has a Ford Escort, registration MDM377F. Would his record appear before or after the one in this example?

   (d)   Copy and complete this table to show which fields are alphabetic, numeric or alpha-numeric.

Field type	Field numbers
alphabetic	
numeric	
alpha-numeric	

2   Why would it not be feasible to use the main file as part of a telephone enquiry service, providing immediate replies to vehicle queries?

3   Explain why a 'deletion' type transaction record needs only two fields.

4   Read the following passage:

"Mr. Perrin's Ford Escort was so old and battered that he
finally had to scrap it. As a replacement he was able to
use his wife's Mini for a few weeks. It was old but reliable
and it did not look too bad now that it had been resprayed
a bright blue instead of the old faded maroon. However,
Mr. Perrin longed to buy another car of his own. His
chance came when his neighbour, Mr. Hill, happened to
mention that he had bought himself a brand new Ford
Cortina and would be selling his old car, a four year old
Maxi. They agreed on a price and Mr. Perrin bought the
Maxi from Mr. Hill".

a.   How many vehicle transaction file records will be
created as a result of the events taking place in the
passage?

b.   Briefly describe each of these records indicating
whether it is an amendment, deletion or insertion.

Collection of data

Data for the transaction file is obtained from two main sources.

In the case of a newly registered vehicle, DVLC receives a
form from a Local Vehicle Licensing Office (LVLO). There are
approximately 50 of these offices throughout the UK with
responsibility for the registration of all new vehicles. The form
V55 is used for this purpose. This is partially pre-completed by
the manufacturer and held by the dealer until the vehicle is
sold. When this happens the dealer completes the form for the
customer, giving all the details of the new vehicle. The form is
presented to the LVLO, where it is checked along with other
documents and the registration mark allocated to the vehicle.
The LVLO then forwards the form V55 to the DVLC for
processing. (See opposite page.)

The processing of this type of data results in the creation of a
main file record for the new vehicle with the Registration
Document being printed and forwarded to the keeper. This
Registration Document provides the keeper with printed details
of his or her vehicle record as stored on the main file tape.

+ 👑

Department of Transport

Please do not write above this line

Application for a First Licence for a Motor Vehicle and Declaration for Registration

S_____ 0350248

V55/5
Rev. June/80

Official Use Only

Receipt Number

Licence Serial Number

Important *In your own interests, before completing this form, please read the booklet 'Notes on Completion of Vehicle Registration Forms' obtainable from Local Vehicle Licensing Offices and main post offices. This booklet explains which questions have to be answered for which class of vehicle. Please complete the form in black ball-point pen or typewriter and in BLOCK LETTERS.*

1 Registration Mark | | 2 | | 3

2 Taxation Class | | | 4

3 Period of Licence Applied for | MONTHS | | 5

4 Duty Payable | £ | | 6

5 Make | | | 9

6 Model | | | 11

7 Type of Body/Vehicle | | 13

8 Wheelplan | | 15

9 Colour(s) | | 17

10 *Hackney Class Only* Seating Capacity (exclusive of Driver) | | 19

11 Date from which Licence is to run (and Date of Registration) — Day Month Year | 7 | Official Use Only | 8

12 Type of Fuel | 10

13 V.I.N./Chassis/Frame No. | 12

14 Engine Number | 14

15 Cylinder Capacity (in cc) | 16

16 Gross Weight — Tons / Kg | 18

17 Unladen Weight — Tons / cwt / lbs / Kg | 20

110 | 111 | Used Re-reg Export Captive Private B'ness Fleet — U R E C P B F | 112

Original Dealer Code | Original Dealer (Name, Address and Postcode) | Selling Dealer Code | Selling Dealer (Name, Address and Postcode)

Type Approval | 113 | Official Use Only — AB 21 WC 22 SN 23 SPMK 24

17a Is the vehicle new?
In either case, please write the last 2 digits of the year of the vehicle's manufacture in this box. | 19 | 25
NOTE If it **is** new, evidence of newness must be supplied in the form of a statement of vehicle particulars from the manufacturer/importer
If it **is not** new, attach an explanation of why it has not previously been registered — Answer YES or NO......

18 If the vehicle is constructed or adapted for the carriage of goods (this includes dual-purpose vehicles of the estate car type) will it be used at any time to carry goods or burden (including samples) for or in connection with a trade or business or for hire or reward? — Answer YES or NO......

19 Will the vehicle be used with a detachable container for carrying goods etc? — Answer YES or NO......

20 Will the vehicle be used to draw a trailer (including a caravan)? — Answer YES or NO......
If the answer is YES will the trailer be used to carry goods or burden (including samples) for or in connection with a trade or business or for hire or reward? — Answer YES or NO......

21 Have any alterations been made of the kind mentioned in the note on this question in the booklet 'Notes on Completion of Vehicle Registration Forms'? — Answer YES or NO......
If the answer is YES were these changes made after the vehicle came into your possession? — Answer YES or NO......

22 Will the vehicle be fitted with alternative bodies? — Answer YES or NO......

If this vehicle is to be registered under a mark from your advance allocation, the form V53 which bears the mark, **must** be affixed to this box

Please now complete the reverse of this sheet | Page 1

13

A second source of transaction data comes from the keepers of the vehicles themselves. They can inform the DVLC of sale, or any changes in vehicle particulars, by using the V5 registration document shown below and on the opposite page.

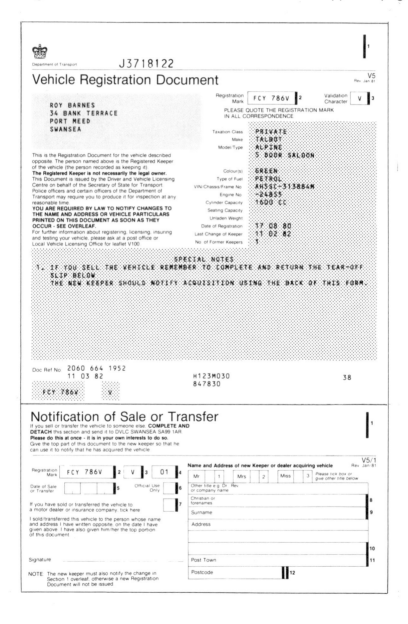

14

Notification of Changes

You must notify changes **IMMEDIATELY** Complete the appropriate section(s) below in **BLACK INK** and **BLOCK LETTERS,** sign the declaration and send the document to DVLC. Swansea SA99 1AR. UNLESS you also require a vehicle licence In this case, the notification must accompany your licence application and be submitted to a licensing post office or Local Vehicle Licensing Office — see licence application form for details.

SECTION 1 - NAME AND ADDRESS OF VEHICLE KEEPER (if different from that printed overleaf).

Mr	1	Mrs	2	Miss	3	Please tick box or state other title below

(a) If your name is different from that shown overleaf please enter new details opposite.

Other title e.g. Dr., Rev., or company name

Christian or forenames   5

Surname   6

(b) If your address is different from that shown overleaf please enter new details opposite.

Address

7

Post Town   8

Postcode   9

(c) If the change is because you are the new keeper please tick this box and give the date you acquired the vehicle. You must also give your name and address in the above boxes if you have not done so already.   K   10

Day	Month	Year

11

Official Use Only   W 4   C D 12

SECTION 2 — VEHICLE SCRAPPED OR PERMANENTLY EXPORTED (if applicable)

Notify scrapping only if the vehicle has been broken up or destroyed by you.
If you notify permanent export a certificate of the vehicle's particulars will be issued.

Please tick the appropriate box   Scrapped   S   Permanently Exported   P   14   and give date of scrapping/export

Day	Month	Year

15   R 13

SECTION 3 — CHANGE OF VEHICLE PARTICULARS (if applicable)

a. NEW UNLADEN WEIGHT (in kilograms) _____ and Date of Weighing

Day	Month	Year

17

b. NEW COLOUR (Basic colour e.g. Red, Green) _____ and Date of Change   19

c. NEW SEATING CAPACITY, EXCLUDING DRIVER (only required if Hackney)   21

d. NEW/REPLACEMENT ENGINE NUMBER   22

e. NEW CYLINDER CAPACITY (in cc's)   23

f. NEW BODY TYPE/WHEELPLAN _____

g. NEW FUEL (e.g. Petrol; Diesel) _____

H 16   U W 18   C L R 20   W/ BT 24   F 25

SECTION 4 — CHANGE OF TAXATION CLASS (if applicable)

Enter new class below and send to a Local Vehicle Licensing Office with a licence application. If the change is to GOODS also complete 3a above; if to HACKNEY also complete 3c.

NEW TAXATION CLASS (e.g. Private; Goods) _____

Y 26   TC 27

DECLARATION

I declare that I have checked the information given on this form and that to the best of my knowledge it is correct.

Signature _____ Date _____

& 28 ISC   29 PR   30
CM   31 MK   32 MD   33
CN   34

This tear-off section must be completed overleaf and sent to DVLC, Swansea, SA99 1AR when you sell or transfer the vehicle. The new keeper must also notify the change, using the top part of this document.

15

If a vehicle is sold the original keeper gives the top half of the V5 to the new keeper, who completes the name and address portion on the reverse of the form and despatches it to the DVLC The former keeper fills in the bottom part of the V5 (the 'notification of sale or transfer') and sends it to the DVLC to advise them.

Other transactions include:

— change of name;

— change of address;

— vehicle scrapped or permanently exported;

— change of vehicle particulars, e.g. colour change.

Any of the above changes can be conveyed to the DVLC by the keeper filling in the changes sections on the reverse of the V5 and despatching it to the centre.

Questions

5   When registering a new car the dealer completes form V55 and sends it to DVLC. What type of transaction record will be created?

6   What is the main function of Local Vehicle Licensing Offices?

7   DVLC will record a change in vehicle keeper only when the two forms have been received. What are the two forms? Why does the centre need them both?

8   Refer to the passage of question 4 in exercise 2. For each event listed in your answer, explain how DVLC acquires the information.

Data Preparation

Data preparation starts when incoming mail arrives at the Mail Receipt Section (MRS) of the DVLC. For the purposes of this study we are primarily concerned with the mail that affects vehicle registrations but DVLC receives many other types of document such as driving licence applications and details of vehicle licences (car tax) issued from Post Offices. About 200,000 items of post arrive every day.

Before being coded, all data received at the DVLC must be put through a flowline system of stringent clerical checks. Any application still with cheques, postal orders or vouchers attached is examined for any obvious errors. If an error is found, the application is sent back to the sender, with a note pointing out the mistake. This process is also carried out for all V5 documents (e.g. changes in keeper details). If any errors are located these documents are also returned to their source for correction and subsequent re-submission.

In order to keep a record of all documents received at the DVLC and to minimise the vast amount of storage space they would otherwise take up, they are microfilmed. The original documents can now be destroyed.

The microfilm cameras print a number unique to each document as it is being photographed and that number appears on the computer record and also on the driving licences and vehicle registration documents. The reason for this is to enable copies of individual applications to be recovered quickly, from the microfilm library, for audit purposes.

The microfilming retrieval operation is reported to be the largest of its kind in Europe. Mistakes are found in about 5% of all application documents so locating and rectifying as many errors as possible at this stage will speed up processing later.

The next task involves converting the batches of microfilmed documents into computer-readable form. The conversion is performed by key punch operators using a special direct data entry key-to-disc system. The operators key data into eight small computer systems wherein it is temporarily held on magnetic disc. This converted data is then transferred to magnetic tape so that it can be loaded onto the mainframe computer system for subsequent processing.

The system performs extensive error checking at all levels of data input. Once again, picking up errors at this stage can save a great deal of time and effort later on. Error checking or data vetting, as it is sometimes called, is carried out in three different ways.

1   Foreground Vetting — This is carried out by the screen format program which only allows data to be entered into the system in a certain predefined manner. The keyboard operator selects the format program required for the different types of data.

2   Verification — Batches of data are keyed then rekeyed by different operators. As rekeying occurs the data is compared and any inconsistency is signalled to the operator for correction.

3   Background Vetting — The verified batches of data held on the disks are checked for errors. This program generates an error report which can be examined clerically. The errors are then corrected.

The data preparation stage can be summarised by the diagram opposite.

receive mail

check for errors

key onto magnetic disc

microfilm

transfer to tape
for processing

19

Questions

9 Suggest some clerical checks that may be carried out as forms arrive at DVLC.

10 Why are the forms microfilmed?

11 Until 1975 the centre used paper tape equipment for data preparation. What advantages does the present key-to-disc system have over the old paper tape system?

Computer processing

The tapes from the data preparation department contain the unsorted transaction records for that day. They are normally ready by early evening at which time they are loaded onto the mainframe computer system in order to update the vehicle main file. The update is executed by a suite of programs, each one carrying out a specific task. A much simplified description of the update follows and serves to illustrate some of the main functions of the process.

Task one — data vet

This is the first program in the update suite and its purpose is to identify errors which have slipped through the data preparation stage, and to check items on the transaction records that can only be checked at this stage. E.g. vehicle has valid registration number, or make and model of vehicle are correct. The data vet program creates a new magnetic tape file of vetted (checked) data. If errors are reported by the data vet, then the transactions are checked before being resubmitted to the system. The diagram opposite shows the flowchart for the data vet program.

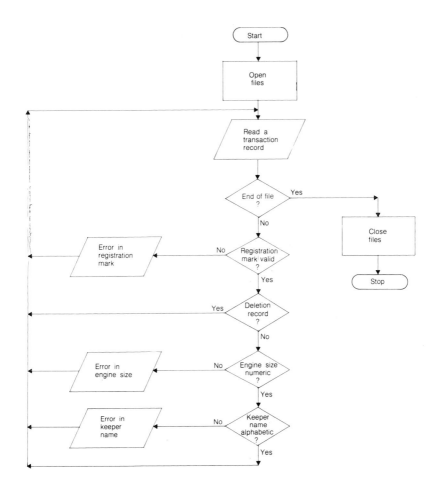

Data vet (simplified)

Task two — sort

As the main file is held on magnetic tape it has to be updated serially. This involves searching the file from beginning to end in order to insert, delete or amend records in the correct positions according to the registration marks. Clearly this operation is practical only if the transaction records are in the same sequence as the main file records. Consequently, task two of the program suite is to sort the transaction records into registration mark order.

Task three — main file update

Main file records to be processed are read into the main store of one of the computers in the system, updated and written back onto a new magnetic tape file. New vehicle records may be inserted by writing them onto the new tape file in their appropriate positions according to the registration marks. Records are deleted by not copying them across onto the new tape file.

At the end of the program a new updated vehicle main file exists on magnetic tape. This file is then used as input for the next update on the following day.

Let us now consider in more detail the processing involved in inserting, amending and deleting records from the vehicle main file.

Inserting a record

The record to be inserted is read from the transaction file into the main store of one of the computers together with the record from the main file. The record key fields are now compared. If the main file record key is less than the transaction record key, then the main file record is written to the new main file tape. The next record is now read from the vehicle main file and the comparison repeated. However, if the key of the record to be inserted has the lesser value then it is written onto the new main file tape. If a transaction registration number matches that of a main file record i.e. trying to insert a record that exists, the main file record is 'frozen' automatically by the program. Transactions cannot be processed against a frozen record.

This ensures that no computer reports or documents are produced with incorrect information.

The process of insertion can be seen in the simplified flowchart below.

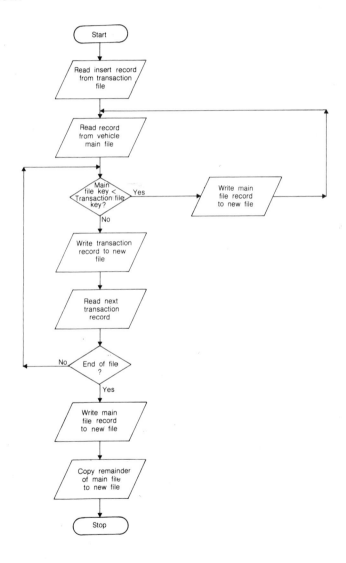

Inserting records into vehicle main file

Amending a record

Typical amendments include changes in vehicle details, taxation class or keeper's address.

The amendment record is read from the transaction file into main store together with a record from the vehicle main file. The keys of the two records are compared. If they are not the same then the main file record is written to the new main file tape. When the two keys are equal, the field is amended in main store and the amended record is written to the new main file tape.

Deleting a record

The record to be deleted is read from the transaction file into main store together with a main file record and the record keys are compared. If a match does not occur then the main file record is written to the new main file tape. However, if the keys are equal then the main file record is not written to the new main file. This is shown in the flowchart below.

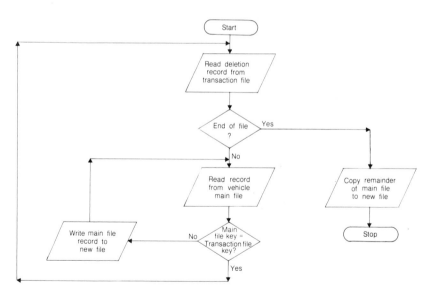

Deleting records from vehicle main file

24

It must be noted that the flowcharts shown only provide a very simplistic view of the serial update process. In reality a single program handles insertions, amendments and deletions. This program also caters for such errors as attempting to delete or update a non-existent record.

Questions

12 Copy the table shown below.

END OF FILE ?	VALID REGISTRA- TION ?	DELETION RECORD ?	ENGINE SIZE NUMERIC ?	KEEPER NAME ALPHABETIC ?	OUTPUT
NO	YES	NO	NO		ERROR IN ENGINE SIZE

Now use the flowchart on page 21 to complete the table showing the effect of the data vet program on the following transaction records. The first one has been done for you.

a. I PFF811J   1E00   BRIAN WELCH

b. A CKD139W   2000   ALAN FOX

c. D BMD433F

d. A TBR199R   1300   ANN BIGG5

e. D BMM MM

f. I 01? ()   997

g. END OF FILE

13   Copy the table shown below.

TRANSACTION FILE	MAIN FILE	MAIN KEY TRANSACTION KEY ?	NEW MAIN FILE
DAN488X	CKD831C	YES	CKD831C

Now use the flowchart on page 23 to complete the table showing the process of inserting new records. Use the following data:

Transaction file keys   Main file keys

DAN488X   CKD831C
JMD31T   CPN441L
JXR144R   HLM66M
END OF FILE   KKR14S
                               LDS36F

14   Copy the table shown below.

TRANSACTION FILE	MAIN FILE	MAIN KEY = TRANSACTION KEY	NEW MAIN FILE

Now use the flowchart on page 24 to complete the table showing the process of deleting records. Use the following data:

Transaction file keys   Main file keys
(all deletions)

FLO39K   BML415P
HOP776P   BMP428G
MIC33T   FLO39K
END OF FILE   GED140X
                               HOP776P
                               MIC33T
                               VON22E

Output and despatch

The daily update run produces not only a new main file but also thousands of registration documents for records that have been inserted or amended. However, the volume of stationery that has to be produced is so great that the computer linked printers would not be able to cope. In order to overcome this problem the update run does not actually print documents. Instead it produces print tapes containing all the information that would be printed onto registration documents. These tapes are then transferred to the off-line printing section which consists of eleven printers, each independent of the main computer system. The printers are very complex, each containing a mini-computer to control its operation. Using suitable programs it is possible for a printer to locate and print part of a batch, or sort through a tape and print out specific types of document. The printer also produces documents in post code order, so that out-going mail is partially sorted when it is handed over to the Post Office.

The registration documents now have to be posted to the vehicle keepers. All outgoing mail, including the registration documents, are at this stage still in continuous stationery form. At the despatch section this stationery is cut and folded into individual licences and registration documents. These are then inserted, together with other appropriate materials, into envelopes. All processes in this section are carried out mechanically by efficient paper handling machinery. The envelopes are then collected by the Post Office for despatch throughout Great Britain.

The printing section

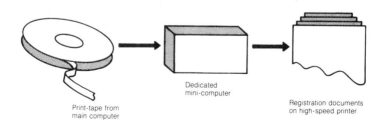

Print-tape from
main computer

Dedicated
mini-computer

Registration documents
on high-speed printer

The centre has eleven of these systems.

Questions

15 Describe the function of the off-line printing section.

16 Why does the centre use off-line printing instead of using printers connected to the mainframe system?

Outline of the vehicle registration system

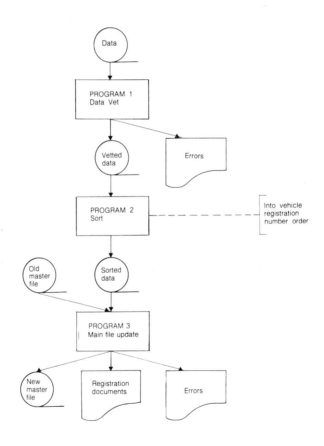

Chapter 3: Functions of DVLC information

The DVLC is able to provide individuals and organisations with information from its files. However, it is important that the centre should not allow unauthorised access to information.

To ensure that all the data on the DVLC computer systems remains confidential the following precautions are taken:

— stringent checks are made on both input data and enquiries;

— all enquiries are suitably authorised and are subject to close scrutiny;

— access to the main file tapes is restricted to authorised personnel;

— no personal information (e.g. medical history of drivers) is held on the computer system. (In fact driver medical records are not even held at the centre.)

Subject to these restrictions information may be provided for the following people.

The registered keeper

Every week the DVLC receives a very large number of enquiries from people wishing to trace the history of their vehicles. For example, the keeper may wish to know how many owners the vehicle has had, who the previous owner was or whether the vehicle has been modified at any time. After verifying that the enquiry has come from the registered keeper, the details are coded onto the appropriate document. Documents are then batched, microfilmed and submitted to the computer system in the usual way. The computer produces a copy of the vehicle main file record including a reference to any relevant information in the centre's microfilm library. Finally, a copy of the appropriate details is despatched to the keeper. This procedure takes approximately ten days from the date when the DVLC receives the enquiry.

Police

The DVLC provides the Police National Computer with particulars of all motor vehicles registered in the UK. This includes details of the present keeper and the descriptive details of the vehicle. This is accomplished by the interchange of magnetic tapes. The police provide the DVLC with details of stolen motor-vehicles which are not recovered quickly and any that have been recovered.

Ticket offices

The Ticket offices are responsible for the collection of fines arising from parking offences etc. A number of the larger Ticket offices submit magnetic tapes (daily or weekly) to the DVLC, listing the registration numbers of the vehicles involved in order to acquire the particulars of the present keepers and the details of the vehicles. Replies are returned daily on magnetic tape.

Manufacturers and traders

Copies of first registration forms (V55) excluding keeper details are sent to the Society of Motor Manufacturers and Traders. They are used for statistical and marketing purposes. One important function of this co-operation is that if new vehicles of a certain type are found by the manufacturer to have a serious fault, the manufacturer can use the DVLC to locate the keepers of these vehicles so that they can be recalled.

Department of Transport

The DVLC provides monthly statistical returns of first registrations, and also conducts the annual vehicle census.

Other bodies with which the DVLC exchanges information include local authorities, government departments, insurance companies and HM Customs and Excise.

Questions

1   The Police National Computer is supplied with details of all registered vehicles. For what purposes do you think this information might be used?

2   Ticket offices do not keep their own vehicle file. Instead, they request particular vehicle details as the need arises. Would this method be suitable for providing the police with information? Explain your answer.

3   Some vehicle details are not stored on computer files. How are these details stored?

Chapter 4: A micro-computer simulation

The program that you are going to use simulates some of the activities involved in the vehicle registration system.

Ten options are available within the program. You may make your selection by pressing the number that represents the required option.

1   Add items to master file

2   Sort master file

3   Prepare transaction file

4   Sort transaction file

5   Update master file

6   New transaction file

7   Output master file

8   Search master file

9   New master file

10   Return to outer menu

Task 1 — Creating a transaction file

Copy the form shown on page 36. This is a simplified version of form V55, the one used for registering new vehicles. Complete the form using details of your family car or a car that you would like to own. Using option 3 of the program, this information may now be keyed onto disc and will become part of the vehicle transaction file.

Notice what happens if the operator keys in an invalid taxation class such as PRIVXT instead of PRIVAT.

Once all of the forms have been entered, the records should be sorted using option 4. You now have a vehicle transaction file on magnetic disc.

Task 2 — Updating the vehicle main file

Option 5 should now be selected in order to update the master file. Inspect the updated file using option 7 and notice the insertions that have been made. At the same time if a printer is available you can obtain your vehicle registration document.

Of course, a real transaction file contains amendments and deletions as well as insertions. Using option 6, delete the transaction file and create a new one containing records of all three types. Update the master file.

Task 3 — Searching the file

You have been given a parking ticket and you have failed to pay the fine within the permitted time. Consequently, the Ticket office, knowing only your car registration number, has requested your name and address from DVLC.

Use option 8 of the program to find names and addresses from given registration numbers.

Other typical enquiries could include:

—   records of all GREEN vehicles on file;

—   records of all VOLVO vehicles;

—   the record of a particular keeper by name.

Declaration for Motor Vehicle Registration

Registration Mark

Make

Model

Colour

Taxation Class

Name of Keeper

Address of Keeper

Signature_____ Date_____